How many?　Counting to 5

0	1	2	3	4	
0	1	2	3	4	5

☐ umbrellas

☐ buckets

☐ fish

☐ frog

☐ loaves

☐ cakes

How many? Counting to 5

0	1	2	3	4	5
0	1	2	3	4	5

☐ bus

☐ bicycles

☐ beds

☐ chairs

☐ lions

☐ elephants

Counting to 5

Colour 2

Colour 4

Colour 1

Colour 5

Colour 3

Colour 4

Counting to 5

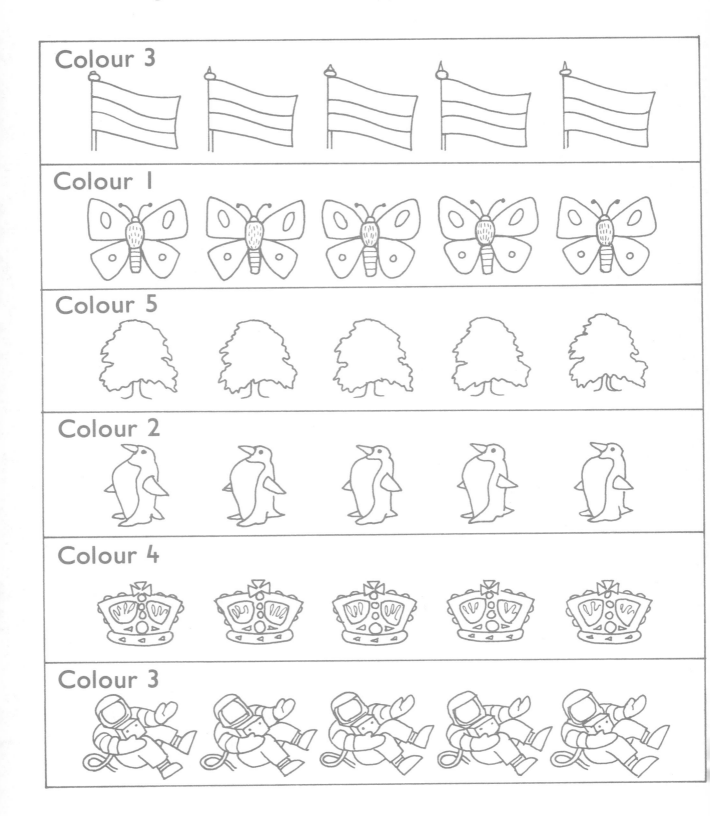

Colour 3

Colour 1

Colour 5

Colour 2

Colour 4

Colour 3

Add + to 5

1 + 2 → ☐

1 + 1 → ☐

3 + 2 → ☐

1 + 4 → ☐

2 + 2 → ☐

1 + 3 → ☐

4 + 1 → ☐

2 + 1 → ☐

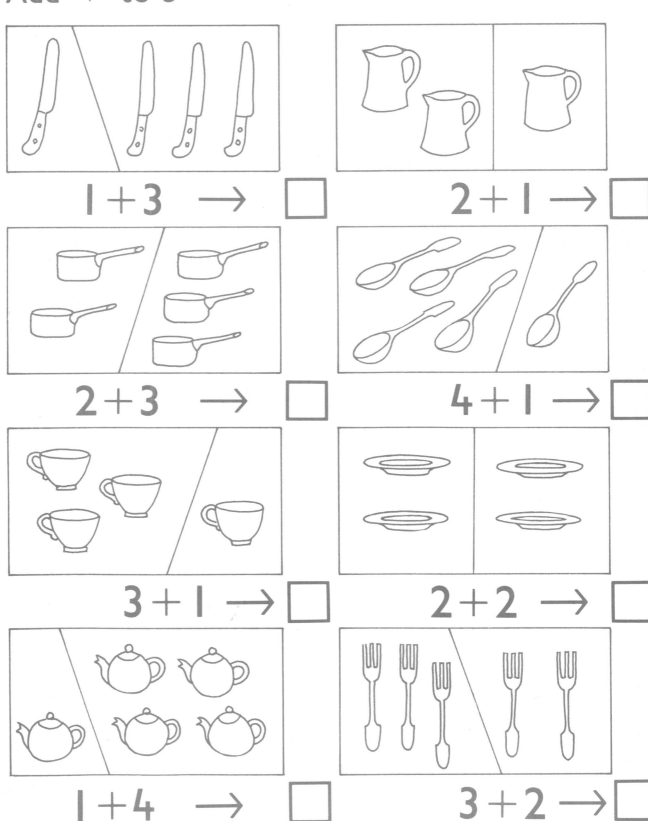

Add + to 5

1 + 3 → ☐

2 + 1 → ☐

2 + 3 → ☐

4 + 1 → ☐

3 + 1 → ☐

2 + 2 → ☐

1 + 4 → ☐

3 + 2 → ☐

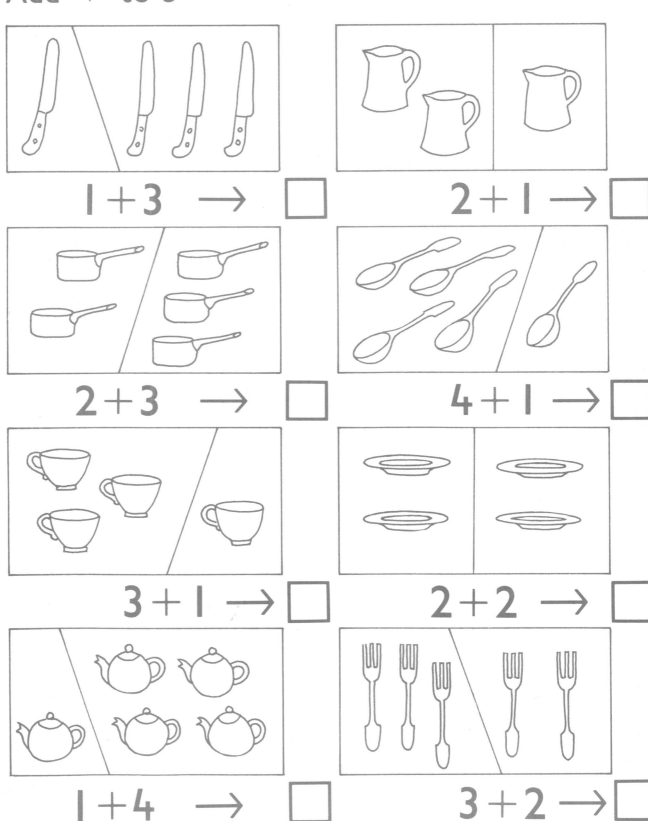

Count and add + to 5

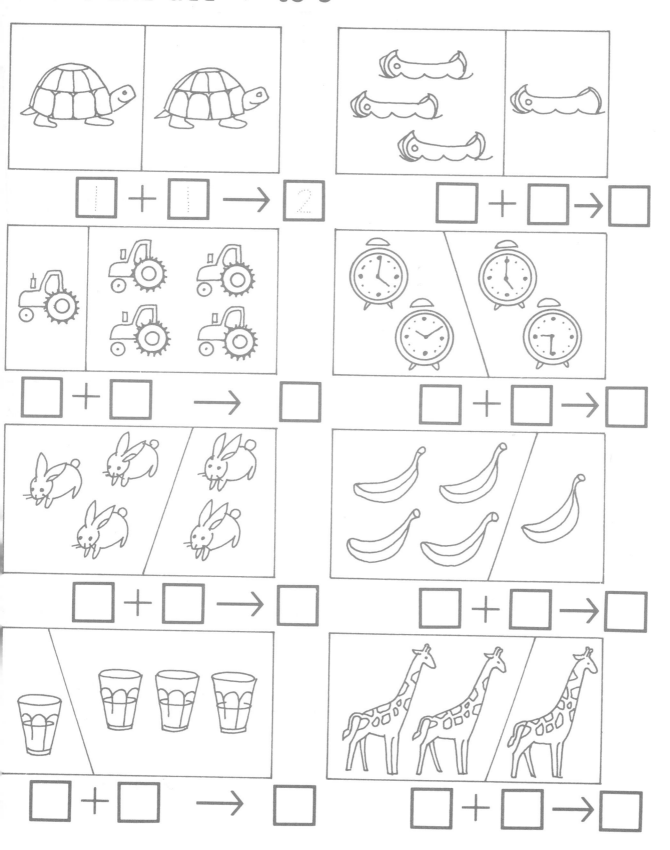

Count and add + to 5

Use counters to take away —

take away 1 ☐ left

take away 1 ☐ left

take away 2 ☐ left

take away 1 ☐ left

take away 3 ☐ left

take away 2 ☐ left

Use buttons to take away —

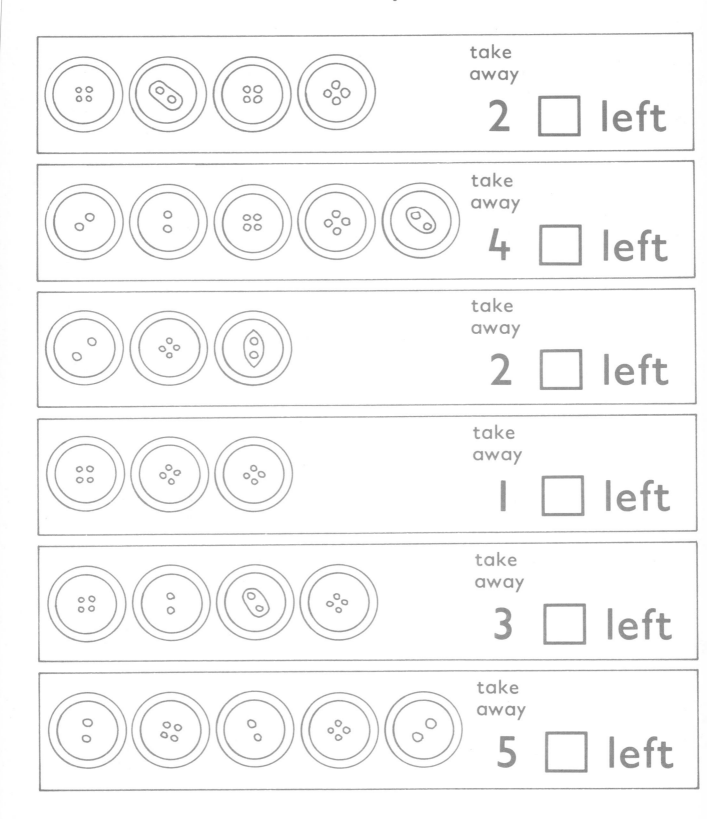

take away 2 ☐ left

take away 4 ☐ left

take away 2 ☐ left

take away 1 ☐ left

take away 3 ☐ left

take away 5 ☐ left

Take away —

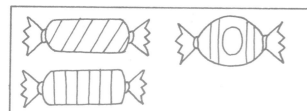 3 take away 1

 $3 - 1 \rightarrow \square$

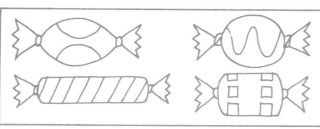 4 take away 1

 $4 - 1 \rightarrow \square$

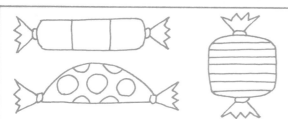 3 take away 2

$3 - 2 \rightarrow \square$

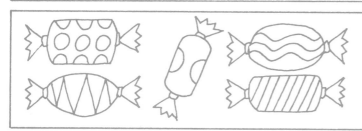 5 take away 1

$5 - 1 \rightarrow \square$

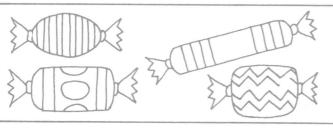 4 take away 3

$4 - 3 \rightarrow \square$

 5 take away 4

$5 - 4 \rightarrow \square$

Add + Revision to 5

$$1 \quad + \quad 1 \quad \rightarrow \quad 2$$

$1+1 \rightarrow \boxed{2}$	$1+2 \rightarrow \boxed{}$	$1+3 \rightarrow \boxed{}$
$1+4 \rightarrow \boxed{}$	$2+2 \rightarrow \boxed{}$	$2+3 \rightarrow \boxed{}$
$2+1 \rightarrow \boxed{}$	$1+1 \rightarrow \boxed{}$	$3+1 \rightarrow \boxed{}$
$3+2 \rightarrow \boxed{}$	$4+1 \rightarrow \boxed{}$	$1+3 \rightarrow \boxed{}$
$2+2 \rightarrow \boxed{}$	$2+3 \rightarrow \boxed{}$	$1+2 \rightarrow \boxed{}$

Take away −

$$3 \quad - \quad 1 \quad \rightarrow \quad 2$$

$1-1 \rightarrow \boxed{0}$	$2-1 \rightarrow \boxed{}$	$3-1 \rightarrow \boxed{}$
$3-2 \rightarrow \boxed{}$	$2-2 \rightarrow \boxed{}$	$3-3 \rightarrow \boxed{}$
$4-1 \rightarrow \boxed{}$	$4-2 \rightarrow \boxed{}$	$4-3 \rightarrow \boxed{}$
$4-4 \rightarrow \boxed{}$	$5-1 \rightarrow \boxed{}$	$5-2 \rightarrow \boxed{}$
$5-5 \rightarrow \boxed{}$	$5-3 \rightarrow \boxed{}$	$5-4 \rightarrow \boxed{}$

How many?   Counting to 10

0	1	2	3	4	5	6	7	8	9	10
0	1	2	3	4	5	6	7	8	9	10

☐ birds

☐ trees

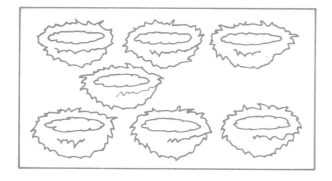

☐ nests

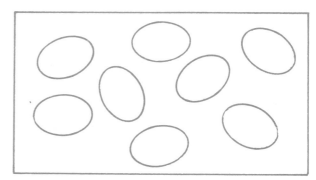

☐ eggs

☐ nuts

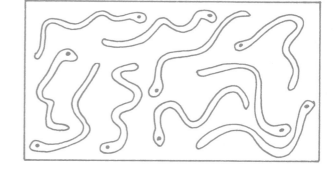

☐ worms

How many? Counting to 10

0	1	2	3	4	5	6	7	8	9	10

☐ sheep

☐ ducks

☐ hens

☐ horses

☐ cows

☐ pigs

How many? Count and colour

0	1	2	3	4	5	6	7	8	9	10
0	1	2	3	4	5	6	7	8	9	10

Colour   6 kites

Colour   8 ice-creams

Colour   5 buckets

Colour   7 sandcastles

Colour   9 flags

How many?   Count and colour

0	1	2	3	4	5	6	7	8	9	10
0	1	2	3	4	5	6	7	8	9	10

Colour   7 acorns

Colour   6 bears

Colour   10 caterpillars

Colour   9 drums

Colour   8 eyes

How many? Add + to 10

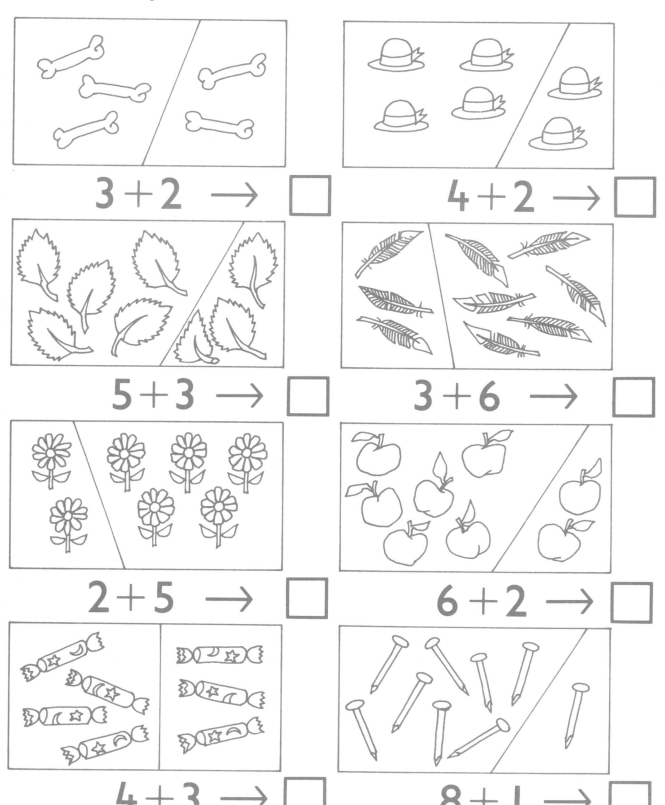

3 + 2 → ☐

4 + 2 → ☐

5 + 3 → ☐

3 + 6 → ☐

2 + 5 → ☐

6 + 2 → ☐

4 + 3 → ☐

8 + 1 → ☐

How many? Add + to 10

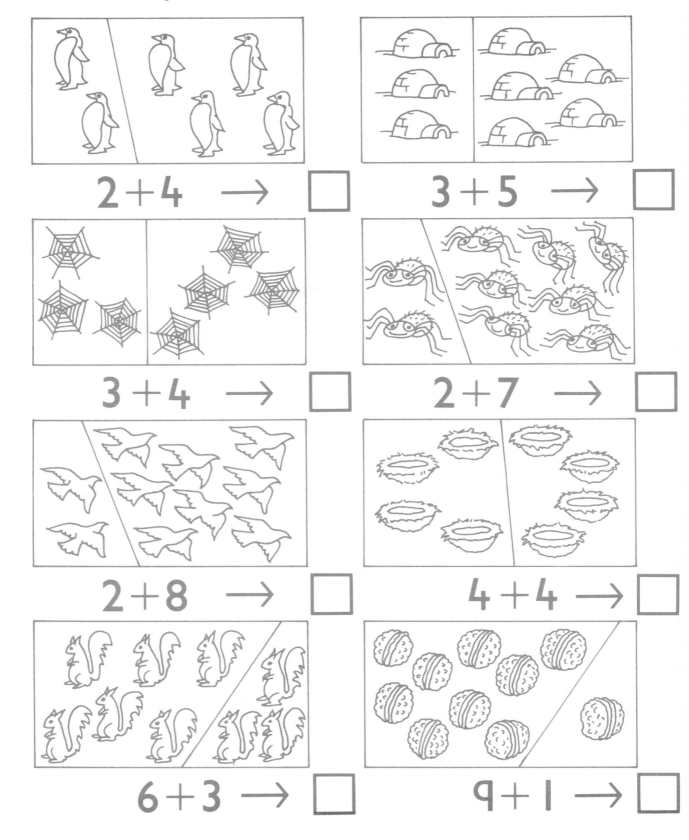

2+4 → ☐

3+5 → ☐

3+4 → ☐

2+7 → ☐

2+8 → ☐

4+4 → ☐

6+3 → ☐

9+1 → ☐

How many? Add + to 10

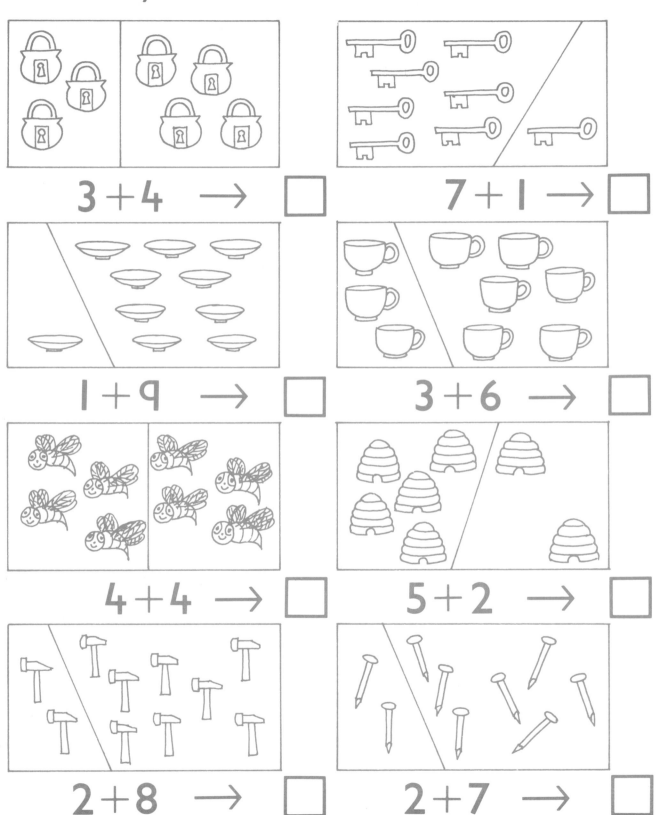

3 + 4 → ☐

7 + 1 → ☐

1 + 9 → ☐

3 + 6 → ☐

4 + 4 → ☐

5 + 2 → ☐

2 + 8 → ☐

2 + 7 → ☐

How many? Add + to 10

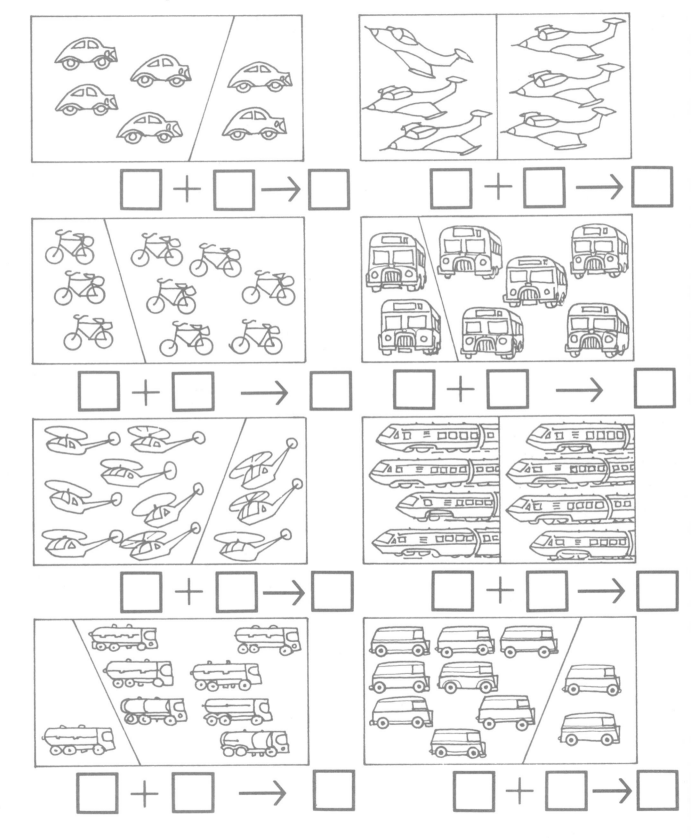

How many? Add + to 10

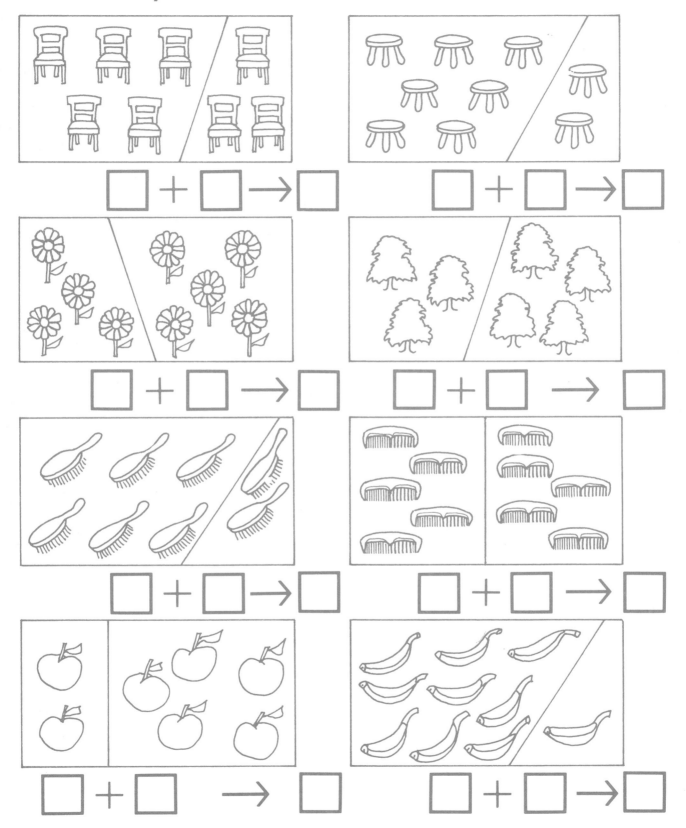

How many? Draw and add + to 10

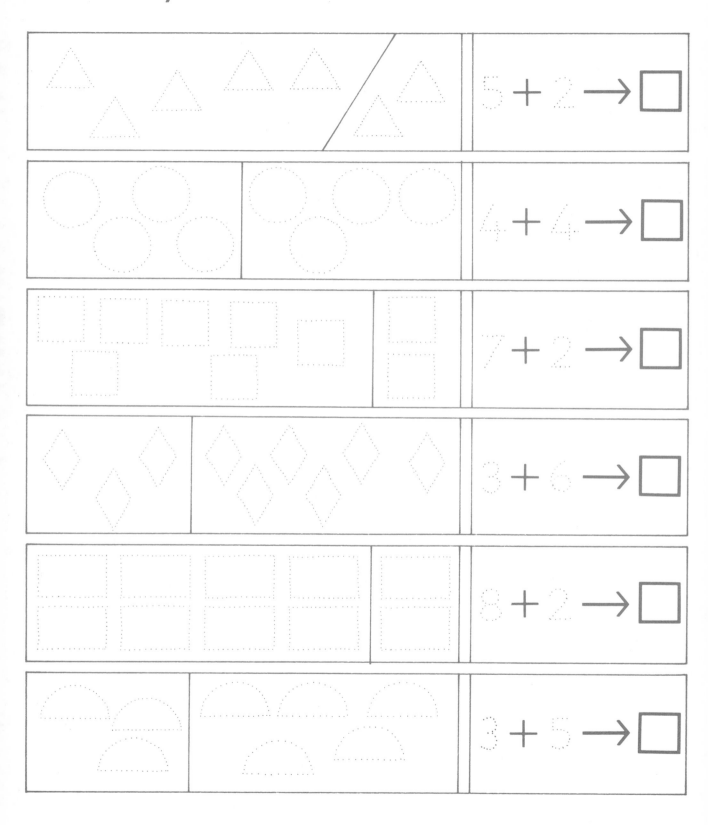

$5 + 2 \rightarrow \square$

$4 + 4 \rightarrow \square$

$7 + 2 \rightarrow \square$

$3 + 6 \rightarrow \square$

$8 + 2 \rightarrow \square$

$3 + 5 \rightarrow \square$

How many? Draw and add + to 10

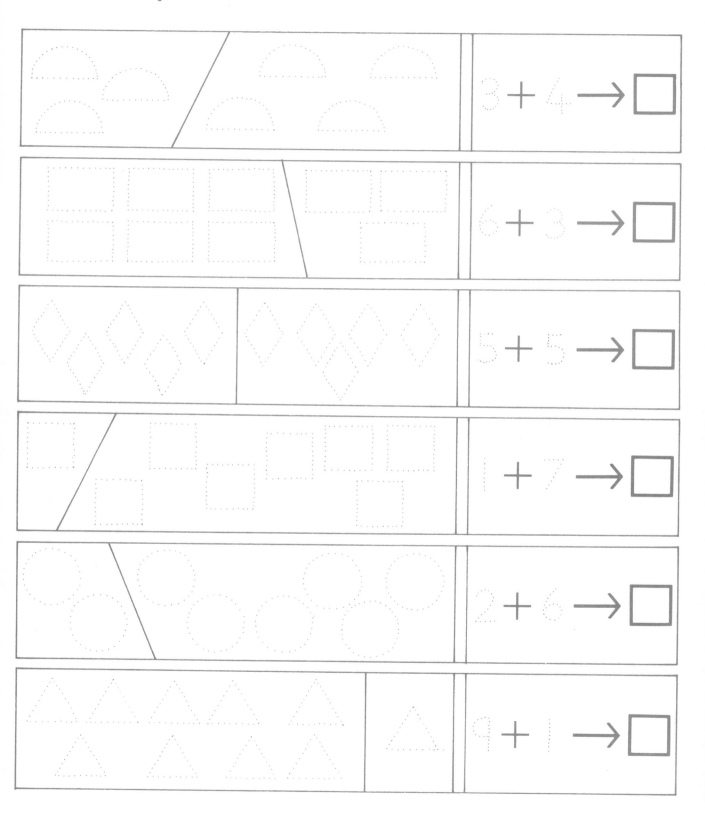

$3 + 4 \rightarrow \square$

$6 + 3 \rightarrow \square$

$5 + 5 \rightarrow \square$

$ + 7 \rightarrow \square$

$2 + 6 \rightarrow \square$

$9 + 1 \rightarrow \square$

Use counters to take away —

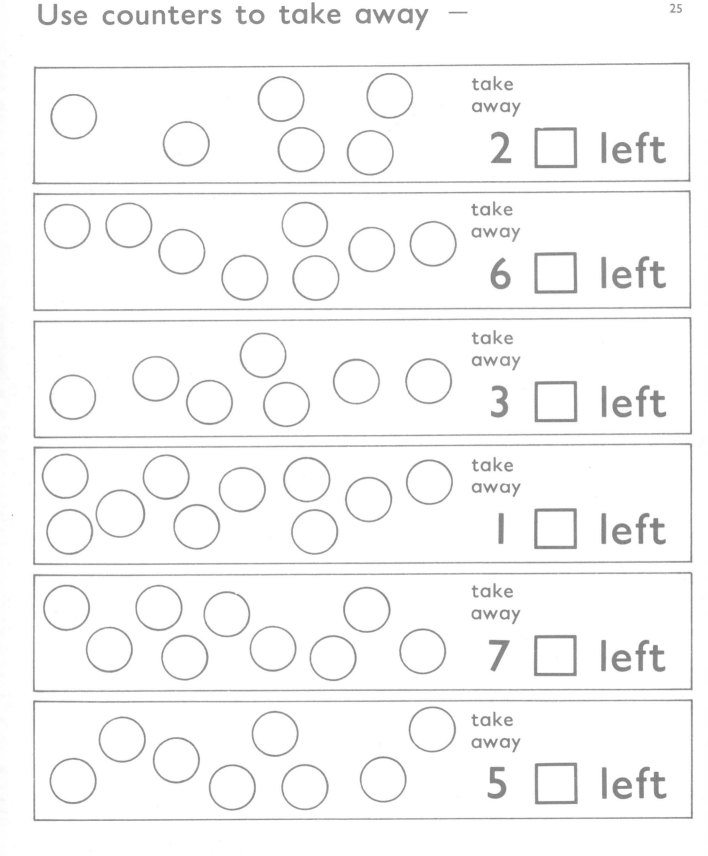

take away **2** ☐ left

take away **6** ☐ left

take away **3** ☐ left

take away **1** ☐ left

take away **7** ☐ left

take away **5** ☐ left

Use buttons to take away −

take away **5** ☐ left

take away **7** ☐ left

take away **3** ☐ left

take away **1** ☐ left

take away **4** ☐ left

take away **5** ☐ left

Take away −

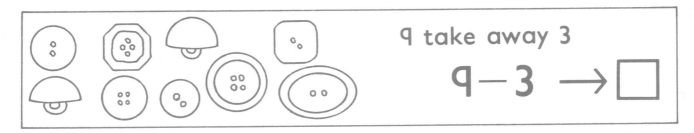

9 take away 3

$$9 - 3 \rightarrow \square$$

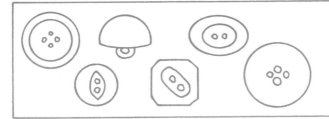

6 take away 3

$$6 - 3 \rightarrow \square$$

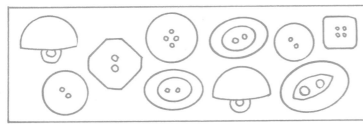

10 take away 6

$$10 - 6 \rightarrow \square$$

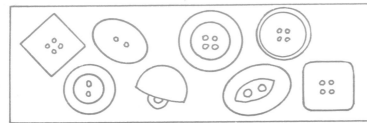

8 take away 5

$$8 - 5 \rightarrow \square$$

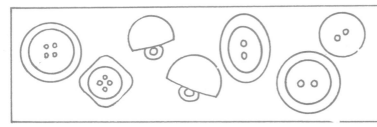

7 take away 7

$$7 - 7 \rightarrow \square$$

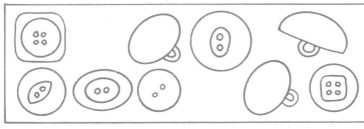

9 take away 7

$$9 - 7 \rightarrow \square$$

Take away –

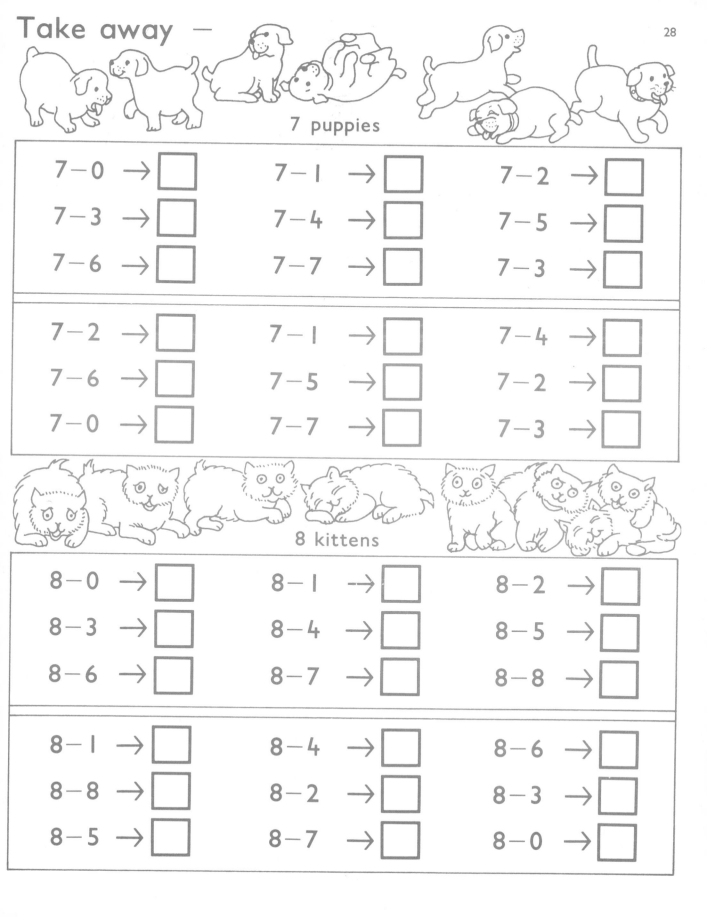

7 puppies

7 − 0 → ☐	7 − 1 → ☐	7 − 2 → ☐
7 − 3 → ☐	7 − 4 → ☐	7 − 5 → ☐
7 − 6 → ☐	7 − 7 → ☐	7 − 3 → ☐

7 − 2 → ☐	7 − 1 → ☐	7 − 4 → ☐
7 − 6 → ☐	7 − 5 → ☐	7 − 2 → ☐
7 − 0 → ☐	7 − 7 → ☐	7 − 3 → ☐

8 kittens

8 − 0 → ☐	8 − 1 → ☐	8 − 2 → ☐
8 − 3 → ☐	8 − 4 → ☐	8 − 5 → ☐
8 − 6 → ☐	8 − 7 → ☐	8 − 8 → ☐

8 − 1 → ☐	8 − 4 → ☐	8 − 6 → ☐
8 − 8 → ☐	8 − 2 → ☐	8 − 3 → ☐
8 − 5 → ☐	8 − 7 → ☐	8 − 0 → ☐

Take away —

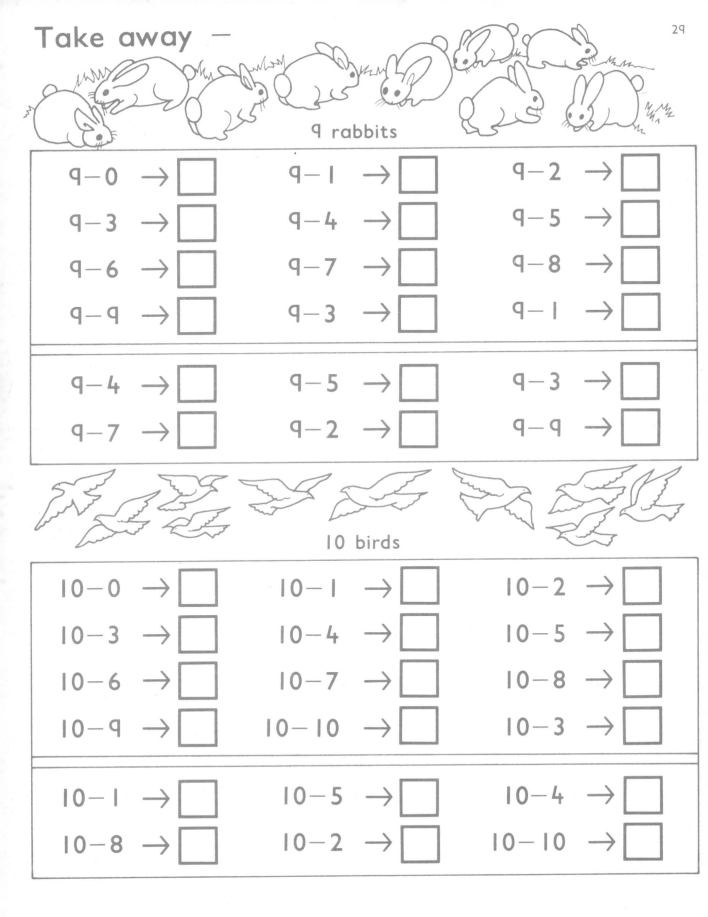

q rabbits

q−0 → ☐   q−1 → ☐   q−2 → ☐

q−3 → ☐   q−4 → ☐   q−5 → ☐

q−6 → ☐   q−7 → ☐   q−8 → ☐

q−q → ☐   q−3 → ☐   q−1 → ☐

q−4 → ☐   q−5 → ☐   q−3 → ☐

q−7 → ☐   q−2 → ☐   q−q → ☐

10 birds

10−0 → ☐   10−1 → ☐   10−2 → ☐

10−3 → ☐   10−4 → ☐   10−5 → ☐

10−6 → ☐   10−7 → ☐   10−8 → ☐

10−q → ☐   10−10 → ☐   10−3 → ☐

10−1 → ☐   10−5 → ☐   10−4 → ☐

10−8 → ☐   10−2 → ☐   10−10 → ☐